# PYOTR IL'YICH TCHAIKOVSKY

# VIOLIN CONCERTO

D major/D-Dur/Ré majeur
Op. 35

Edited by
Richard Clarke

## Ernst Eulenburg Ltd

London · Mainz · Madrid · New York · Paris · Prague · Tokyo · Toronto · Zürich

# CONTENTS

# PREFACE

In the early part of 1878 Tchaikovsky, staying at Clarens, received a visit from his former pupil, the violinist Yosif Kotek. The weather was bad and they played through a great deal of music together, both piano duets and violin with piano; among other things, they played Lalo's *Symphonie espagnole* for violin and orchestra which – as Tchaikovsky wrote to Mme von Meck (3/15 March) – gave him great pleasure. Two days later, although he had only just begun the Piano Sonata in G, he set about the composition of a violin concerto of his own, obviously in emulation of Lalo's 'freshness, lightness, piquant rhythms, beautiful and admirably harmonised melodies'; it was the first time he had ever embarked on a new composition before finishing one already begun, he told Mme von Meck, but he wanted to take advantage of Kotek's presence. His letters to his brother Anatoly also tell us about the progress of the concerto: 'It will be a new and difficult task for me, but interesting all the same'. And on 8/20 March, 'The concerto is moving – not very quickly, but it's moving'. Two days later he was able to announce to Mme von Meck:

The first movement of the Violin Concerto is already finished. Tomorrow I shall set about the second. Ever since the day when the auspicious mood came upon me, it has not left me. In such a phase of spiritual life composition completely loses the character of work; it is pure enjoyment. While you're writing you don't notice how the time is passing, and if no one came to interrupt the work you would sit all day without getting up.

On 16/28 March the concerto was 'finished in the rough' and the next day Tchaikovsky began to copy it out.

The following excerpts from letters to Anatoly tell their own story:

I've finished copying out the first movement of the concerto and I played it in the evening. Modest [his brother] and Kotik [='Tomcat': nickname for Kotek] were both in absolute raptures, I was very pleased with the ovation they gave me (20 March/1 April).

Kotek has managed to copy out the violin part of the concerto and we played it before dinner. The success was tremendous both for the composer and performer. Actually Kotek played as if he were just going to give a public performance. […] In the evening he played the *Andante*, which pleased me much less than the first movement. As a matter of fact, I'm not particularly satisfied with it myself (22 March /3 April).

The finale of my concerto creates a furore among us, but we've rejected the *Andante* and tomorrow I shall have to write a new one (23 March/4 April).

(The 'rejected' *Andante* was later published as a 'Meditation' for violin and piano, Op. 42, No. 1.)

I have written a new *Andante* with which both my severe but sympathetic critics are satisfied. […] With what love he [Kotek] fusses over my concerto! Needless to say that without him I shouldn't have been able to do anything. He plays it marvellously (24 March/5 April).

I'm working hard at the instrumentation of the concerto (25 March/6 April).

The date on the autograph score shows that the orchestration was finished on 30 March/11 April.

Tchaikovsky would have liked to dedicate the concerto to Kotek, but, he told his publisher Jurgenson, 'in order to avoid gossip of various kinds' (gossip that was not without foundation) 'I shall probably decide to dedicate it to *Auer*. In no circumstances to Wieniawski or any other celebrity. I like Auer very much both as artist and as a man' (letter of 1/13 July). He had already dedicated his *Sérénade mélancolique* for violin and orchestra to him. A week later or so he decided: 'I shall dedicate the concerto to Auer'. What happened next is best told in Auer's own words:

Tchaikovsky […] came to see me one day in St Petersburg to show me a concerto for violin and orchestra which had already been engraved and was ready for circulation, and which bore the dedication 'A Monsieur Leopold Auer'.

Profoundly touched by this mark of his friendship, I thanked him warmly and at once had him sit down at the piano, while I, seating myself beside him, followed with feverish interest his somewhat awkward piano rendering of the score. I could hardly grasp the entire content of the work at this first audition; but was at once struck by the lyric beauty of the second theme in the first movement, and the charm of the sorrowfully inflected second movement, the 'Canzonetta'. Tchaikovsky left the music with me, upon my promise to study the work and to play it at the first opportunity. When I went over the score in detail, however, I felt that, in spite of its great intrinsic value, it called for a thorough revision, since in various portions it was quite unviolinistic and not all written in the idiom of the strings. I regretted deeply that the composer had not shown me his score before having sent it to the engraver, and determined to subject it to a revision which would make it more suited to the nature of the violin, and then submit it to the composer. I was eager to undertake this work as soon as possible; but a great deal happened to prevent my getting to it, and I decided to lay it aside for a short time.

I had just been offered the directorship of the symphonic concerts of the Russian Musical Society. [...] This new position, in addition to all my other work, pre-empted all my time and energy: I was obliged to make up programmes for the entire season, to choose the solo artists – and the correspondence carried on with them was by no means the least part of my duties – and attend to a thousand and one other managerial details. Naturally, the Tchaikovsky concerto suffered. In fact, I deferred the matter of its revision so thoroughly, that after waiting two whole years, the composer, very much disappointed, withdrew the original edition. Quite frankly, admitting that I was to blame, I thought him perfectly within his rights.

It had originally been intended that Auer should play the concerto at a Russian Musical Society concert on 10/22 March 1879. Then Kotek and Emile Sauer wanted to give it, but these performances also were abandoned – Tchaikovsky believed owing to pressure from Auer.

The concerto had begun to be spoken of as unplayable when it was taken up by a younger man, Adolph Brodsky, who told the story himself in a letter to the composer:

It has been my dream to play this concerto in publi ever since the minute I read it through for the fir time. That was two years ago. Several times I s about it but broke off; indolence defeated my will attain my goal. You've piled up so very many diff culties! Then last year, being in Paris, I played th concerto to Laroche so badly that he couldn't gras it properly, but all the same he approved of it. [.. On my return to Russia I set about the concerto r ally energetically. How delightful it is! – one ca play it endlessly and never weary! This is very im portant if one is to conquer its difficulties. When seemed to me that I knew it well enough, I decide to try my luck in Vienna.

After trying it out at a *Novitätenprobe* unde Richter, Brodsky had been allowed to make hi Viennese début with the concerto at the Phil harmonic Concert on 4 December 1881. It wa the only one of Tchaikovsky's works to be playe abroad before it had been heard in Russia. Th reception was mixed and very stormy, but th applause dominated over the disapproval an Brodsky was called back three times. The re ception by the critics was on the whole hostile Hanslick's outstandingly offensive one in th *Neue Freie Presse*, with its reference to 'stinking music' in the finale, has often been quoted; i wounded Tchaikovsky so deeply that he knew it by heart to the end of his life. But one or tw voices were more friendly; Oskar Berggrün i the *Morgenpost* hailed it as 'one of the mos original and effective' of violin concertos an the anonymous critic of the *Wiener Abendpos* wrote that:

The wildly fantastic Violin Concerto by Tchaikovsky divided the audience for and against this origina production. The first movement with its splendid healthy themes, the mysterious quiet middle movemen (who could fail to be reminded by this of Turgenev' female characters!), and the wild peasant dance make up a whole for which we would claim an outstanding place among contemporary compositions.

Brodsky next introduced the concerto to London at a Richter Concert (8 May 1882), and to Russia (Moscow, 8/20 August 1882), and in gratitude Tchaikovsky re-dedicated the work to him Then Kotek rather shamefacedly played it i

Moscow, not very successfully. Next it was taken up by Karol Halir in Prague and Joseph Marsick in Paris. It was not until 1893, a few months before the composer's death, that Auer played the concerto in public; he also performed it at the Tchaikovsky Memorial Concert on /18 November. Later still he published his long-delayed 'revision'. According to his autobiography, it

as been played in that form by all my older pupils on oth sides of the Atlantic. I often played it in Europe, as I had revised it, and thus – after a sufficiently protracted delay, for which I trust Tchaikovsky's *manes* will forgive me – I have kept the word I gave the great Russian composer long years ago.

Tchaikovsky sold the concerto for 50 roubles to Jurgenson, who brought out an arrangement for violin and piano in October 1878, the orchestral parts in August 1879, and the full score in June 1888.

Gerald Abraham

# VORWORT

Anfang 1878 erhielt Tschaikowsky, der sich in Clarens aufhielt, Besuch von seinem früheren Schüler, dem Geiger Josef Kotek. Da das Wetter schlecht war, spielten sie verschiedenerlei Musik durch, sowohl für Klavier zu vier Händen, als auch für Violine und Klavier. Darunter war auch Lalos *Symphonie espagnole*, die Tschaikowsky, wie er am 3./15. März an Frau von Meck schrieb, viel Vergnügen bereitete. Zwei Tage darauf machte er sich, obgleich er eben erst die Klaviersonate in G begonnen hatte, an die Komposition eines eigenen Violin-Konzerts, offenbar in Nachahmung von Lalos Frische, Leichtigkeit, prickelnden Rhythmen und bewundernswerten Melodien. Es war das erste Mal, dass er eine Komposition begann, bevor er die vorhergehende beendet hatte, so sagte er Frau von Meck, doch wollte er Koteks Anwesenheit nutzen. Die Briefe an seinen Bruder Anatol berichten auch vom Fortgang des Werkes: „Es wird eine neue und schwere Arbeit für mich sein, aber jedenfalls interessant." Und am 8./20. März: „Das Konzert kommt nicht schnell vorwärts, aber es kommt vorwärts". Zwei Tage später konnte er an Frau von Meck berichten:

Der 1. Satz des Violin-Konzerts ist schon fertig. Morgen will ich den 2. in Angriff nehmen. Seitdem die günstige Stimmung über mich kam, hat sie mich nicht verlassen. In einer solchen Phase des geistigen Lebens verliert das Komponieren den Charakter der Arbeit; es ist reines Vergnügen. Während man schreibt, merkt man nicht, wie die Zeit vergeht, und wenn niemand unterbrechen würde, könnte man den ganzen Tag dabei bleiben.

Am 16./28. März war das Konzert im Rohbau fertig, und am nächsten Tag fing er an, es zu kopieren.

Die folgenden Auszüge aus Briefen an Anatol erzählen ihre eigene Geschichte:

Ich habe die Abschrift des 1. Satzes des Konzerts beendet und spielte es am Abend. Modest [sein Bruder] und Kotik [Kater, Spitzname für Kotek] waren beide hingerissen. Ich war sehr froh über die Ovation, die sie mir gaben. (20. März/3. April)

Kotek hat die Violinstimme des Konzerts abgeschrieben, und wir spielten es vor dem Essen. Der Erfolg war sowohl für den Spieler als auch für den Komponisten enorm. Tatsächlich spielte Kotek, als ob unmittelbar eine Aufführung bevorstände. [...] Am Abend spielte er das *Andante*, das viel weniger gefiel als der 1. Satz. Ich bin wirklich nicht sehr zufrieden mit mir selbst. (22. März/3. April)

Das Finale des Konzerts hat für Furore unter uns gesorgt, aber wir haben das *Andante* verworfen, und morgen will ich ein neues schreiben. (23. März/4. April)

(Das „verworfene" *Andante* wurde später als *Méditation* für Violine und Klavier, Op. 42 No. 1, veröffentlicht.)

Ich habe ein neues *Andante* geschrieben, mit dem meine beiden strengen, aber wohlwollenden Kritiker zufrieden sind. [...] Mit welcher Liebe befasst er [Kotek] sich mit meinem Konzert! Unnötig zu sagen, dass ich ohne ihn nichts hätte tun können. Er spielt es wundervoll. (24. März/5. April)

Ich arbeite schwer an der Instrumentation des Konzerts. (25. März/5. April)

Das Datum auf der autographen Partitur zeigt, dass die Instrumentation am 30. März/11. April beendet war.

Tschaikowsky hätte gern das Konzert Kotek gewidmet, aber, so sagte er seinem Verleger Jurgenson, „um Gerüchte verschiedener Art zu vermeiden" (die nicht ganz ohne Grund waren) „werde [ich] mich wahrscheinlich entschließen, es Auer zu widmen, keinesfalls Wieniawski oder irgendeiner anderen Berühmtheit. Ich liebe Auer als Künstler und als Mensch" (1./13. Juli). Er hatte ihm schon seine *Sérénade mélancolique* für Violine und Orchester gewidmet. Etwa eine Woche darauf beschloss er: „Ich will das Konzert Auer widmen." Was dann geschah, erzählt sich am besten in Auers eigenen Worten:

Tschaikowsky suchte mich eines Tages in St. Petersburg auf, um mir ein Violin-Konzert zu zeigen, das schon gestochen und zur Verbreitung bereit war und die Widmung trug: „A Monsieur Leopold Auer".

Tief gerührt von diesem Zeichen der Freundschaft, dankte ich ihm warm und nötigte ihn, sich ans Klavier zu setzen, während ich, daneben sitzend, mit fieberhaftem Interesse seine etwas ungeschickte Wiedergabe der Partitur auf dem Klavier verfolgte. Ich konnte bei diesem ersten Hören kaum den ganzen Gehalt des Werkes erfassen, war aber sofort ergriffen von der lyrischen Schönheit des 2. Themas des 1. Satzes, und dem Charme des schwermütigen 2. Satzes, der *Canzonetta*. Er ließ die Noten bei mir gegen mein Versprechen, das Werk zu studieren und bei erster Gelegenheit zu spielen. Als ich jedoch die Partitur genauer studierte, empfand ich, dass trotz des großen, inneren Wertes, eine gründliche Revision nötig war; denn es war in verschiedenen Teilen gar nicht geigerisch und nicht für die Eigenart des Streichinstruments geschrieben. Ich bedauerte sehr, dass der Komponist mir die Partitur nicht gezeigt hatte, bevor sie gestochen wurde, und beschloss, sie einer Revision zu unterziehen, die sie besser spielbar machen würde, und sie dann dem Komponisten vorzulegen. Ich wollte diese Arbeit so bald als möglich ausführen, aber vieles hinderte mich daran, und ich entschloss mich, sie für kurze Zeit beiseite zu legen.

Mir war gerade die Direktion der Symphonie-Konzerte der Russischen Musik-Gesellschaft angeboten worden. […] Diese neue Stellung, zusammen mit all meiner sonstigen Arbeit, nahm alle meine Zeit und Kraft in Anspruch: Ich war verpflichtet, die Programme für die ganze Spielzeit aufzustellen, die Solisten auszuwählen – und die Korrespondenz mit diesen war nicht der geringste Teil meiner Aufgaben – sowie tausenderlei Verwaltungsarbeiten auszuführen. Natürlich litt das Tschaikowsky-Konzert darunter. Tatsächlich verschob ich die Revision so lange, dass der Komponist nach zweijährigem Warten, sehr enttäuscht, die ursprüngliche Widmung zurückzog. Ich gab offen zu, dass ich zu tadeln und er in seinem Recht sei.

Nach dem ursprünglichen Plan sollte Auer das Werk in einem Konzert der Musik-Gesellschaft am 10./22. März geben. Dann wollten es Kotek und Emile Sauret spielen, aber diese Aufführungen wurden ebenfalls fallen gelassen – wie Tschaikowsky annahm, auf Druck von Auer.

Man munkelte bereits, das Werk sei unspielbar, bis es von einem jüngeren Mann, Adolf

Brodsky, aufgenommen wurde, der darüber i einem Brief an den Komponisten schrieb:

Von der ersten Minute, in der ich das Werk durchsa war es mein Traum, es öffentlich zu spielen. Das w vor zwei Jahren. Einige Male fing ich damit a brach aber immer wieder ab. Mein Wille wurd durch Trägheit gehemmt. Die Schwierigkeiten sin so gehäuft! Dann spielte ich es letztes Jahr in Par Laroche vor, aber so schlecht, dass er es nicht richti erfassen konnte. Trotzdem billigte er es. […] Nac meiner Rückkehr nach Russland machte ich mic mit neuer Energie daran. Wie wunderbar es ist! Ma kann es endlos spielen und wird nicht müde! Das i sehr wichtig, wenn man die Schwierigkeiten übe winden will. Als ich glaubte, es gut genug zu könne beschloss ich, mein Glück in Wien zu versuchen.

Nachdem er es bei einer Novitätenprobe unte Richter ausprobiert hatte, wurde Brodsky ge stattet sein Wiener Debüt mit diesem Konzert z geben, und zwar im Philharmonischen Konze am 4. Dezember 1881. Es war das einzige Wer Tschaikowskys, das im Ausland früher gespiel wurde als in Russland. Die Reaktionen ware gemischt und sehr stürmisch, aber der Beifa überwog die Missbilligung, und Brodsky wurd dreimal gerufen. Die Reaktion der Presse wa im Ganzen feindlich. Die besonders verletzend von Hanslick in der *Neuen Freien Presse* mi ihrer Anspielung auf „stinkende Musik" im Fi nale, ist oft zitiert worden. Sie hat Tschaikowsk so tief gekränkt, dass er sie bis ans Ende seine Lebens im Gedächtnis behalten hat. Aber einig waren freundlicher: Oskar Berggrün begrüßt es in der *Morgenpost* als eines der originellste und wirkungsvollsten Violin-Konzerte, und de anonyme Kritiker in der *Wiener Abendpos* schrieb:

Das wild phantastische Violin-Konzert von Tschaikow sky teilte das Publikum für und gegen diese originell Schöpfung. Der erste Satz mit seinen glänzenden gesunden Themen, der mysteriöse, ruhige 2. Sat (wer würde dabei nicht an Turgenevs weibliche Cha raktere erinnern?) und der wilde Bauerntanz ergebe ein Ganzes, dem man einen hervorragenden Platz i der modernen Komposition einräumen muss.

ls nächstes führte Brodsky das Konzert in
ondon ein, in einem Richter-Konzert am 8. Mai
882, und in Russland (Moskau, 8./20. August
882). Aus Dankbarkeit änderte Tschaikowsky
ie Widmung daher auf seinen Namen. Später
pielte Kotek es eher beschämt in Moskau –
hne viel Erfolg. Weiter wurde es von Karel
Ialir in Prag und von Joseph Marsick in Paris
ufgenommen. Erst 1893, wenige Monate vor
'schaikowskys Tod, spielte Auer das Konzert
ffentlich; auch führte er es bei einem Gedenk-
onzert für Tschaikowsky am 6./18. November
uf. Viel später noch veröffentlichte er die
ange aufgeschobene „Revision". Nach seiner
Autobiographie

wurde es in dieser Form von allen meinen älteren
Schülern auf beiden Seiten des Atlantic gespielt. Ich
habe es nach meiner Revision oft in Europa gespielt
und somit – nach einer langen Verzögerung, die mir
Tschaikowskys Manen vergeben mögen – das Versprechen gehalten, das ich dem großen, russischen
Komponisten vor langer Zeit gegeben hatte.

Tschaikowsky verkaufte das Konzert für 50
Rubel an Jurgenson, der im Oktober 1878 eine
Ausgabe für Violine und Klavier herausbrachte,
ferner im August 1879 die Orchesterstimmen
und im Juni 1888 die Partitur.

Gerald Abraham

# PRÉFACE

Début 1878, alors qu'il séjournait à Clarens, Tchaïkovski reçut la visite de son ancien élève, le violoniste Josef Kotek. A cause du mauvais temps, ils jouèrent beaucoup de musique ensemble, à la fois pour piano à quatre mains et pour violon et piano, et déchiffrèrent, entre autres, la *Symphonie espagnole* de Lalo pour violon et orchestre dont Tchaïkovski écrivit à Mme von Meck (lettre du 3/15 mars) qu'elle lui procura le plus grand plaisir. Dès le 5/17 mars, bien que son travail sur la Sonate pour piano en sol n'en fût qu'à ses débuts, il entreprit la composition de son propre concerto pour violon, visiblement influencé par « la fraîcheur, la légèreté, les rythmes piquants, les belles mélodies admirablement harmonisées » de l'œuvre de Lalo et confia à Mme von Meck que, voulant profiter de la présence de Kotek, il s'attaquait pour la première fois à une œuvre nouvelle avant d'avoir terminé la précédente. Il décrivit également les étapes de progression du concerto dans ses lettres à son frère Anatoly : « Ce sera une tâche nouvelle et ardue pour moi, mais tout aussi intéressante », et le 8/20 mars : « Le concerto avance – pas très vite mais il avance. » Il fut en mesure, deux jours plus tard, d'annoncer à Mme von Meck :

Le premier mouvement du Concerto pour violon est déjà terminé. Demain, je me mets au deuxième. Depuis le jour où ce souffle propice m'envahit, il ne m'a pas quitté. Dans une telle période d'inspiration, la composition perd complètement son caractère laborieux, c'est un pur bonheur. Vous ne réalisez pas le temps qui passe pendant que vous écrivez et si personne ne venait vous interrompre, vous pourriez rester assis toute la journée sans vous lever.

Le « brouillon » du concerto fut achevé le 16/28 mars et Tchaïkovski commença à le recopier dès le lendemain.

Ces extraits de lettres adressées par le compositeur à Anatoly retracent d'eux-mêmes la chronologie des jours suivants :

J'ai fini de recopier le premier mouvement du concert et je l'ai joué le soir. Modeste [son frère] et Kotik [= « matou », surnom de Kotek] en ont été tous deux enthousiasmés et j'ai été très heureux de l'ovation qu'ils m'ont réservée. (20 mars/1er avril)

Kotek a réussi à copier la partie de violon du concerto et nous l'avons joué avant le dîner. La réussite est extraordinaire autant pour l'interprète que pour le compositeur. En fait, Kotek l'interpréta comme s'il allait l'exécuter en public. […] Dans la soirée, il joua l'Andante, qui me plut beaucoup moins que le premier mouvement. En réalité, je n'en suis moi-même pas particulièrement satisfait. (22 mars/3 avril)

Le Finale de mon concerto fait fureur parmi nous, mais nous avons rejeté l'Andante et je devrai en écrire un nouveau demain. (23 mars/4 avril)

(L'Andante écarté fut plus tard publié sous le titre de *Méditation* pour violon et piano, op. 42, n° 1.)

J'ai écrit un nouvel Andante dont mes deux sévères mais sympathiques critiques sont contents. […] Avec quelle passion il [Kotek] encense mon concerto ! Il va sans dire que sans lui je n'aurais rien pu faire. Il le joue merveilleusement. (24 mars/5 avril)

Je travaille dur à l'instrumentation du concerto. (25 mars/6 avril)

La date inscrite sur la partition autographe du concerto indique que l'orchestration en fut terminée le 30 mars/11 avril.

Tchaïkovski aurait souhaité dédier le concerto à Kotek mais, ainsi qu'il s'en ouvrit à son éditeur Jurgenson, « de manière à éviter les rumeurs de toutes sortes, » (rumeurs loin d'être infondées) « je vais sans doute le dédier à Auer. En aucun cas à Wieniawski ou toute autre célébrité. J'aime bien Auer, à la fois comme artiste et comme homme ». Auer lui-même, dans son autobiographie, fournit la meilleure relation de ce qui se passa ensuite :

Tchaïkovski […] vint me voir un jour à Saint-Pétersbourg pour me montrer un concerto pour violon et orchestre, déjà gravé et prêt à la diffusion, qui portait la dédicace « A Monsieur Leopold Auer ».

Profondément touché par cette marque d'amitié, je le remerciai chaleureusement et le fis sans attendre asseoir au piano, et, assis derrière lui, je suivis fiévreusement son interprétation quelque peu maladroite de sa partition. Je ne pus saisir la totale plénitude de l'œuvre lors de cette première audition, mais fus immédiatement frappé par la beauté lyrique du deuxième thème du premier mouvement et par le charme attristé du deuxième mouvement Canzonetta. Tchaïkovski me laissa sa musique contre ma promesse de l'apprendre et de la jouer dès que possible. Toutefois, quand j'étudiai la partition en détail, je sentis qu'en dépit de sa grande valeur intrinsèque, elle nécessitait une révision minutieuse car plusieurs passages n'en étaient pas du tout violonistiques et ne respectaient pas l'écriture des cordes. Je regrettai amèrement que le compositeur ne me l'ait pas montrée avant de l'envoyer au graveur et décidai d'y apporter des retouches qui la rendraient plus adaptée à la nature du violon, puis de la soumettre au compositeur. Malgré mon impatience d'entreprendre cette tâche le plus vite possible, de nombreux évènements m'en empêchèrent et je la mis de côté à ce moment-là.

Je venais d'être nommé à la tête des concerts symphoniques de la Société russe de musique. […] Ce nouveau poste, ajouté à toutes mes autres activités, monopolisa tout mon temps et mon énergie : je devais établir les programmes de la saison, choisir les solistes – et la correspondance entretenue avec eux ne représentait pas la moindre de mes obligations – et m'occuper de mille et un autres détails d'organisation. Naturellement, le concerto de Tchaïkovski en souffrit. En fait, je reportai tant sa révision qu'après deux années, le compositeur, très déçu, m'en retira l'édition originale. Très franchement, j'admis ma faute et estimai qu'il était parfaitement dans son droit.

Il avait d'abord été décidé qu'Auer jouerait le concerto le 10/20 mars 1879, lors d'un concert de la Société russe de musique. Puis Kotek et Emile Sauret voulurent le donner mais ces projets d'exécutions furent abandonnés – sur la pression d'Auer, de l'avis de Tchaïkovski.

Le concerto commençait à acquérir la réputation d'œuvre injouable quand un jeune violoniste, Adolf Brodsky, s'y attela. Il déclara dans une lettre qu'il adressa au compositeur :

Je rêve de jouer ce concerto en public depuis la m[i]nute où je l'ai déchiffré pour la première fois il y [a] deux ans. Je m'y attaquai plusieurs fois mais m'i[n]terrompis ; l'indolence l'emportait sur ma volont[é] d'atteindre mon objectif. Vous y avez accumulé ta[nt] de difficultés ! Puis, l'an dernier, alors que j'étais [à] Paris, j'ai joué le concerto à Laroche, trop mal qu' [il] put bien le cerner mais qui l'approuva. […] A mo[n] retour en Russie, je me mis vraiment avec énergi[e] au concerto. Quel délice ! On peut le jouer sans cess[e] et ne jamais se lasser ! Ce qui est très important pou[r] en vaincre les difficultés. Quand il me sembla qu[e] je le connaissais assez bien, je décidai de tenter m[a] chance à Vienne.

Après l'avoir présenté lors d'une Novitäten[-]probe sous la direction de Richter, Brodsky fu[t] invité à faire ses débuts à Vienne avec le con[-]certo au Concert philharmonique, le 4 décembr[e] 1881. Ce fut la seule œuvre de Tchaïkovski qu[i] fût donnée à l'étranger avant de l'avoir été e[n] Russie. L'accueil du public fut mélangé et trè[s] agité mais les applaudissements dominèrent le[s] huées et Brodsky fut rappelé trois fois. Les cri[-]tiques y furent dans l'ensemble hostiles et, parm[i] elles, celle ouvertement injurieuse d'Hanslic[k] dans la *Neue Freie Presse* et son allusion à « l[a] musique puante » du Finale ont souvent ét[é] citées. Cette chronique blessa si profondémen[t] Tchaïkovski qu'il put toute sa vie la réciter pa[r] cœur. Cependant quelques voix plus favorable[s] s'élevèrent. Oskar Berggrün, dans le *Morgen[-]post*, décrivit l'œuvre comme « l'un des plu[s] originaux et du plus grand effet » parmi le[s] concertos pour violon et le critique anonym[e] du *Wiener Abendpost* écrivit :

Le sauvagement fantastique Concerto pour violo[n] de Tchaïkovski divisa le public pour ou contre cett[e] production insolite. Le premier mouvement et se[s] thèmes splendides et robustes, le mystérieux et pai[-]sible mouvement central (Qui n'y verrait pas u[n] écho aux personnages féminins de Tourgeniev !) e[t] la danse paysanne effrénée forment un ensemble qu[i] peut se réclamer d'une position singulière parmi le[s] compositions contemporaines.

Brodsky présenta ensuite le concerto à Londres[,] lors d'un concert de Richter (le 8 mai 1882), e[t] en Russie (à Moscou, le 8/20 août 1882)[.]

Tchaïkovski lui exprima sa gratitude en lui re-
médiant l'œuvre. Puis Kotek le joua, assez timi-
dement et sans grand succès, à Moscou. Le
concerto fut ensuite interprété par Karol Halir
à Prague et par Joseph Marsick à Paris. Auer
n'interpréta le concerto en public qu'en 1893,
quelques mois avant la disparition du compositeur et, également, le 6/18 novembre, lors d'un
concert à la mémoire de Tchaïkovski. Il publia
plus tard sa « révision » longtemps ajournée et
révéla dans son autobiographie :

Il a été joué dans cette version par tous mes anciens
élèves de part et d'autre de l'Atlantique. Je l'ai souvent donné en Europe, tel que je l'avais révisé, et,
ainsi – après un retard plutôt prolongé, que, j'en suis
sûr, les mânes de Tchaïkovski me pardonneront –
j'ai tenu la promesse que j'avais faite au grand compositeur russe il y a de longues années.

Tchaïkovski céda le concerto à Jurgenson pour
cinquante roubles. Celui-ci en fit paraître une
réduction pour violon et piano en octobre 1878,
les parties orchestrales en août 1879 et la
grande partition en juin 1888.

Gerald Abraham
Traduction : Agnès Ausseur

# VIOLIN CONCERTO

*À Monsieur Adolphe Brodsky*

Pyotr Il'yich Tchaikovsky
(1840–1893)
Op. 35

I. **Allegro moderato** ♩ = 126

**Ben sostenuto**
**il tempo**

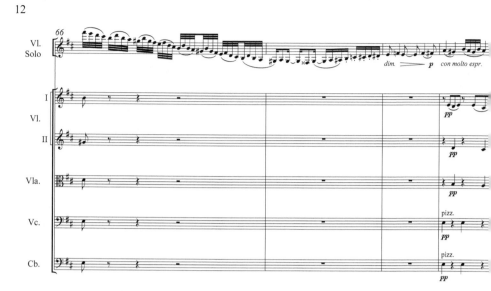

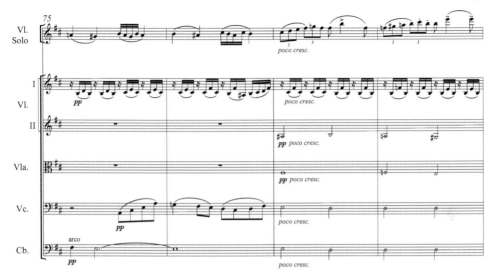

18

20

**Poco più lento**

E **Più mosso**

**molto sostenuto il tempo, moderatissimo**

44

48

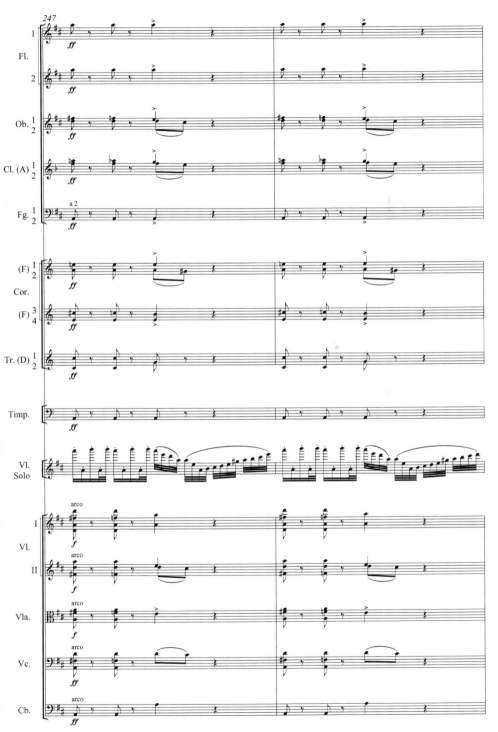

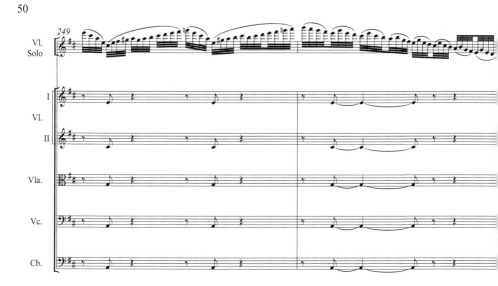

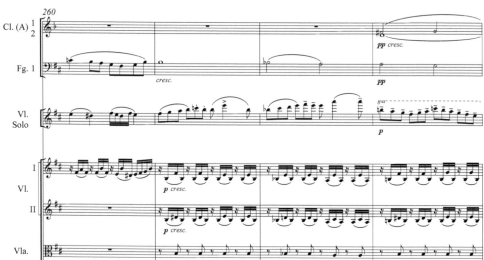

52

EE 3808

**Poco più lento**

N Più mosso

**Allegro giusto**

64

66

**Più mosso**

# II. Canzonetta

**Andante** ♩ = 84

# III. Finale

### Allegro vivacissimo

78

EE 3808

rit.　　Tempo I

EE 3808

**Tempo I**

88

**Tempo I**

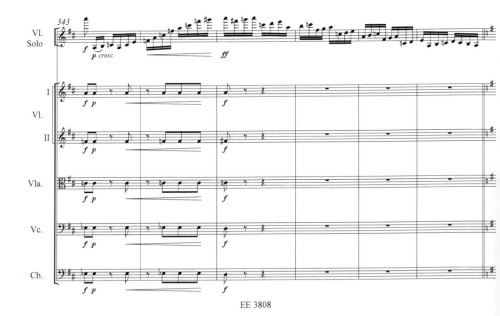

G Poco meno mosso

**Tempo I**

H **Molto meno mosso**

**Poco a poco string.**

EE 3808

118